BEYOND *the* BIKE

MOMMA D. DIAMOND

To Ellen!
Keep shinin Baby!
Love ya!
Momma D

Written by: Momma D. Diamond

ISBN 978-1-0880-8676-6

Photography by: Maggie Hicks

Edited by: Tana Todd

Cover and formatting by: George Paloheimo Jr.

Car: Brian "La Bala" Mendoza

Motorcycle: Momma D. Diamond

TABLE OF CONTENTS

MOMMA D's 33

This book is dedicated to:

God, first, and to my son, Miguel Nieto.
Thanks for having my six, and your unconditional love and support. Last but not least, thank you for helping me relocate to Las Vegas. I love you son.
You are the best, and we make a badass team.

PREFACE

God isn't ready for me yet.

I now realize my *why* and this heartfelt handbook is a way to pass on my knowledge and experiences to help you.

I aspire to inspire until I expire.

FOREWARD

"Dynamic," "exciting" and "highly motivational" are the words that audiences use to describe Momma D.

Momma D. is a professional speaker, published author and motorcycle rider who made history in Honolulu, Hawaii, on September 13, 2006, by becoming the first person in the world to ride the same motorcycle consecutive days, solo, through all 50 United States.

Momma D. is formerly a basketball player, rock 'n roll singer, competitive bodybuilder, dancer, choreographer, exercise physiologist, and clothing designer. Momma D. is a conditioning coach for professional athletes, predominantly in the sports of mixed martial arts and boxing.

Sixty-five in January 2023, - Momma D. has rolled just shy of a million miles in 25 years and has ridden to Fairbanks, Alaska five times. That's ten times rolling up and down the Alaska Highway, and yes, *solo*. She's ridden through all of Canada's Provinces, through Mexico, Spain, Africa and Brazil plus all 50 states twice on two different motorcycles. Those motorcycles sit side-by-side in a display at the National Motorcycle Museum in Anamosa, Iowa.

On display with her motorcycles, there are over 100 photographs of Momma D's historic journeys, and an additional 50 state photographs after completing all 50 states on a second motorcycle Black IEC, in 2016. Alongside her two bikes stands a wax figure of Momma D., two 50-state videos, riding gear, broken motorcycle pieces, and X-rays of her broken bones.

Momma D's accolades include a couple of Lifetime achievement awards, 2021 Top 100 Women in Powersports, and publications in *Biker Alley Magazine, Woman Rider Magazine* and *New Mexico Woman.* In 2004 she was the first woman on a motorcycle on the cover of New Mexico Woman magazine and was also the first woman on the cover of *Get Yonder Magazine* in 2018. She's also appeared in *The Albuquerque Journal, RedRider Magazine, American Motorcyclist Magazine, Woman Riders Now* and *Discover Today's Motorcycling.* In 2021, Momma D. was chosen to lead a group of women on motorcycles from Seattle, Washington to Washington DC, celebrating 100 years of women's right to vote.

Momma D. has been featured on *Entertainment Studios, Urban Style with Samuel L. Jackson,* and *Karl Malone.* She's also been featured in *Smart Women,* a broadcast news series created by women for women, as well as in the TV Pilot of *Harley Nation* and the movie, *Caffeine and Gasoline: Evolution of the American Rocker.*

As a background actor, in 2008, Momma D. appeared in the TV series *Crash and Easy Money*, the movie *Legion* starring Dennis Quaid, *Observe and Report* starring Seth

Rogan and Ray Liotta, and *Doc West*, an Italian western. Momma D. was one of only four women chosen to appear in the TV pilot, *Night and Day*. In the spring of 2009, Momma D. was hired as a background actor for the Warner Brother blockbuster feature film *Terminator Salvation* starring Christian Bale.

In February 2019, she released her first book, *50 States of Consciousness*. It's the true story of Momma D., a momma who defies all stereotypes. It's the story about a 130-pound, six-foot-tall, postmenopausal, motivational African-American who loves country music and rode her 800-pound motorcycle, '*Big Bertha*,' 169 consecutive days, 25,000 miles, through all 50 states, solo, surviving everything from tornadoes to grizzlies, in 2006.

Momma D's second book. *Beyond the Bike*, is full of real-life tactics to be your best you on and off twos, will be released January 2023.

This 5 x 8 handbook covers Momma D's 33, the 33 things that Momma D. does to be Momma D. every single day.

Momma D. is passing on knowledge with humor and she will cover some shocking topics. You'll laugh, learn, and feel a whole gambit of emotions. At the end of each passage, you can make notes and comments when asked, ***"What will you add to your toolbelt?"***

If you have a pulse, there's something inside this heartfelt handbook that will help you or someone close to you.

Are you ready?

Here we go…

"Life's too short to live it giving less than your best. Don't go to your grave with regrets. And no matter how dark life gets, always Keep Shinin' Baby." – Momma D.

#1
Is that a gun in your pocket, or are you just happy to see me?

If I say this to someone and they are offended, that's cool, but we're more than likely not going to be hanging out together.

Here are three examples of people I'd not only hang with, but they are my, bring a smile to my face kind of folks.

When I've asked the question to my buddy Police Officers, their reactions were priceless.

And the last time I said it, the Officer replied, "Both." with a huge smile. Yes, sir, my kind of people.

My next example was an elevated jackpot.

Normally when people are on elevators, no one's talking or making eye contact, but not this time.

Once on an elevator in Vegas, everyone was pushing the buttons for their floors and a young man wanted someone to push the button for the upper penthouse, but he said, "I want the big one."

I couldn't help but say, "That's what she said."

Laughter erupted.

I told him, "You can use that a lot." Another young man said, "That's what *she* said." And everyone had another great belly laugh.

It was one of the coolest elevator rides ever.

Here's one more for you:

My sister, Vanita was a welder in Tulsa, Oklahoma, and loved getting a reaction out of her foreman.

She'd recently got a tattoo of a black panther on her calf.

One morning when she came into work, she decided it was time to hit him with a little morning jolt.

She walked up to the foreman and asked him, "Would you like to see my big black pussy?

She lifted her pant leg and showed him her tattoo.

That poor man almost shit himself, had a heart attack and pissed his pants simultaneously.

He clutched his chest with a sigh of relief and said, "Oh thank you Jesus."

In my opinion, humor should be used to lighten things up, and not to be nasty or rude.

We do not need more hurt. We need more healing to help bring all our crazy asses together, and hopefully we don't kill each other in the process.

My method for *dealing* with life is...I choose truth, love and above all *laughter.*

Like my elevator ride, how do you *deal* with the awkwardness of life - what have you learned and...

What will you add to your tool belt?

____

____

____

____

____

____

____

____

____

#2
Focus on what you can control... your own shit.

Sounds simple, doesn't it?

If it was that simple, then why is it that so many people have their noses up in other folks' business?

When I grew up there were window peepers, not necessarily looking for possible trouble but peeping for some juicy gossip.

Nowadays, it's the keyboard cave dwellers that spy, lurk, stalk, judge, and spew venom who are obviously not focusing on their own shit.

When you have this horrid behavior directed at you, remember it's not actually about you, it's the person projecting their self-loathing and insecurities *onto* you.

Unfortunately, this is even a bigger problem for our young ones.

It's hard enough for adults to deal with bullying and our kids are affected ten-fold.

So, if we as adults are buying into the bull, then how can we help our future generation to rise above the madness.

Addressing this should be high on our to-do list.

Now it's time for me to throw a little wrinkle in the mix.

Here is how much I don't care what folks think of my crazy ass.

Sixty is life expectancy in my family, and with hard work I've already surpassed that digit and I'm shooting for 100!

Of course, as you can image, I won't be what you'd envision, a centenarian to be or act like.

God willin' and the creek don't rise, when I turn that magic number, I will be riding a blacked out, pimped out Can-Am Spyder (a three-wheeled motorcycle with two wheels in front) with a huge skull and spikes on the front.

I'll be sporting fish nets, throwing my leg in the air, just airing it out as I'm rolling down the Vegas strip - flashing my little gray box to the world!

I will get my first tattoo - on my ass no less - and it will say, "Keep shinin' baby."

I'll be pullin' my little granny panties down every chance I get…giving folks a Momma D. show like they've never seen before.

Now, it'll also be time to jump out of a perfectly good plane, with a hot young buck strapped to my back.

And just before we jump, I'll tell him, "Come on baby, jump on and get yourself some! Let's get it!"

Can you see it?!

I can!

Now, let's get back to focusing on what you can control and focusing on your own shit.

What has helped me is…

Knowing everyone isn't going to like me and that's perfectly fine.

If someone disrespects me, I hit block and delete, whether on social media or face-to-face.

Knowing and believing that no one can take my shine.

As we know, it's not always easy but it starts with…caring less about what others think, to focus on what you can control…your *own* shit.

I do.

How about you, what have you learned and...

What will you add to your tool belt?

#3
Squash shade.

Shade is disrespectful.

Why is it that you're supposed to laugh when another female, in disgust, calls you a 'skinny bitch'?

That is not a compliment to me, that is *disrespect.*

Why are we nasty to each other?

I do not understand it but squashing shade head-on is the only way.

Here's an example:

- When I'm called a 'skinny bitch', I shut it down quick. For one thing, I'm not skinny, I'm lean, there's a difference. A skinny body is an inefficient body. I pride myself on being healthy and strong – and a skinny body can't do what I do!

Ladies, we should shine each other's crowns instead of casting shade on them.

We need to get back to the old saying, "Treat others how you'd like to be treated."

Every day I compliment, encourage and lift a sister up. I hope you will do the same.

How about you, do you share your shine or shade?… what have you learned and…

What will you add to your tool belt?

#4
Do these jeans make my butt look big?

Wooooo Nellie! Dayum!

Have you ever said this or had someone ask you this?

To those who have asked this question, do you really want to know, or are you looking to start a fight?

In my opinion, what-ever your ass looks like does not require someone else's approval. No matter if it's big, small, flat or flabby – either own that shit or change it for yourself.

I opt for exercise, not surgery, but if that's something you think you have to do, do you 'boo', I don't judge.

Now for those of you who have been asked, "Do these jeans make my butt look big?"

Lawd a mercy, what do you say?! Especially if you already know the person posing the question is insecure.

You say, "No. They don't. You look hot!"

They come back with, "Yes, they do. You're just saying that. Tell me the truth!"

In all reality, the jeans are not the problem; it's how the person feels *inside.*

You can be nice or mean or whatever, unfortunately it's almost a lose-lose scenario.

Bottom line, pardon the pun…'do these jeans make my butt look big?', is a loaded question.

I'm no frickin' shrink but I know if you don't love yourself (all of you) no one else can or will fix that.

That's on you.

I love myself, flaws and all.

Here's another one of my titillating, make your eyes water visuals ... someday in the future when I'm wearing a bra that's a 36 long, and I'm tucking my tits into my knee-highs…I'll own it baby!

I have never been in this situation but if asked, I'd say, "My opinion shouldn't matter. The way your ass looks in your jeans is on you."

The fact of the matter is…you might not be able to put the fire out on this but there's no need to stoke the kindling either.

How about you, how would you handle this?…what have you learned and…

What will you add to your tool belt?

#5
Feet up – head down.

Inversion.

If you've never heard this word before or know what the hell inversion is, join the club, for years I didn't either.

I have known the health benefits of elevating the feet but when I came upon the benefits of inversion, I was hooked.

Here are a few Inversion health benefits I found…

Inversion can increase blood circulation and lymphatic drainage to help deliver oxygen and nutrients throughout the body and remove waste products.

And here are a couple of ways I've incorporated inversion into my health regimen.

I lay on my back, with my legs raised vertically or I do forearm stands.

Either one I chose to do; it's done for a 5-minute duration.

I admit that when I did the forearm stands the first time, it scared the bejesus out of me.

It was a challenge but the feeling of accomplishing the pose was well worth it.

When I'm traveling on my cross-country motorcycle trips, I prefer the vertical leg raise pose, it's more relaxing for me.

Whether you're on your feet for hours, sitting or riding your motorcycle, elevating and or inversion can be a health benefit.

By simply propping your feet up can make a difference.

Preferably above your heart.

Keep this in mind, these inversion poses might not be for you.

- If you have injuries or health issues, please consult with your doctor before you add these or any new exercises to your regimen.

Please feel free to do a search on the pros and cons of inversion and examples of each.

Speaking of feet up, I recall something someone said to me a few years ago.

I was finishing my glass of wine when a guy standing next to me at the bar said, "The next glass is on me."

I told him, "These days, I'm quite the lightweight.

I appreciate it but I'm good - because if I have more than one glass of wine, my legs fly up in the air."

He said, "Give the lady a bottle."

Feet up – head down is my thing. (Inversion that is)

How about you, what have you learned and...

What will you add to your tool belt?

#6
Peak-a-boo
don't let this be you.

Is it just me or is the world beyond crazy?

It's even more alarming that the sense of security you had because you live in a nice neighborhood has been shot to shit, literally.

No, you shouldn't live in fear every day and every moment in your life, but you should be ready.

I've ridden my motorcycle hundreds of thousands of miles alone and people ask me if I'm packin'.

Blades, yes. Gun, no.

My best weapon is between my ears.

I stay aware of my surroundings and keep my face out of my frickin' phone!

I will do a quick check of my perimeter to make sure no one is close enough to me to get their hands on me.

I have a rule...if you come within arm's length of me without being invited, we are going to have a problem.

I say we because I do not want to throw hands with a grown ass man but if it's him or me, all bets are off.

Unfortunately, I have had issues with several ignorant assholes, out there.

On this occasion, I'd like to share my encounter with a pitiful-punk stunter.

I'd spent a couple of hours dancing at the resort in Mexico, celebrating my divorce.

It was a few minutes before closing, when Mr. 'I'm-a-cool-stunt-motorcycle-rider-dude' struck up a conversation with me and found out that I ride.

Well, he must have been used to the little girls being impressed with his arrogant, cocky ass, but I am a woman that saw he was a complete joke.

He was determined to walk me to my room, to see my view. Mind you, it was 2:00 in the morning.

I told him no, that ain't happening.

Then, the dipshit started to follow me when I left.

I got loud, and if you know me, my loud will fill a football stadium.

He started begging, saying, "I just have to have you!"

I kept a good distance from him and by the time I was close to my room, I was walking backwards to make sure he didn't bum rush me.

I got to my room safe, and thank goodness, he finally went away.

Now, let's say I let that prick into my room and something bad had happened.

That would have been my fault for allowing him in.

But, if he had rushed me and pushed his way into my room, the only view he would have seen would be the spinning stars as he flew ass over teakettle over my balcony.

Peek – a –boo, I see you four floors down.

Please be aware of your surroundings and listen to your gut…if it doesn't feel right, it probably isn't.

Bottom line…use the good sense God gave ya, please pay attention to live and shine another day. I do.

How about you, what have you learned and…

What will you add to your tool belt?

____

____

#7

Don't get your panties in a bunch.

This doesn't apply to me because I don't wear any.

But yes, to this one; are you stressed sometimes?

News flash...there are countless things and people that can and will stress us out.

Of course, that's an understatement.

Here's an example of stress, poison people and some of my ways to cope.

To begin with, back in the day, my drive from Jersey into the City of Manhattan and back daily was an enormous stress within itself.

In 1990, I was hired to manage a Health Club on the upper west side.

Unbeknownst to me, the club owners, husband and wife, were having serious marital problems.

The husband was dating the office manager and leaving with her after work every day.

Now you may be wondering, what does this have to do with me?

Well just a few days of starting my job, each of the staff were pulled into each of their offices and asked which side they were on.

For me, when asked, I said, "It really isn't any of my business. I'm just here to do my job."

Quickly I found out that was the wrong answer, and I now had a target on my back.

Not from her but he started making my life a living hell.

He was also a complete control freak.

With him up my ass constantly, sometimes I would take a break in a bathroom stall.

Despite his harassment, in just the few months, I'd not only successfully run that Health Club, but I'd also built a personal training clientele.

As days passed, he'd gotten so bad I was at my wits end.

One of the trainers noticed my frustration and let me in on a little secret.

I found out the owner was known to bait his managers into a confrontation.

He had NYPD on speed dial and if you hit him, he'd have you taken away in handcuffs.

Shit just got real and I had to have a strategic tactical exit plan.

Knowing his evil plan, I did the professional thing; I handed him my typed two-weeks' notice.

He took it and immediately got in my face baiting me into a confrontation and said, "Leave now!"

My instincts took over.

I was completely calm, and I laughed, which pissed him off more.

He couldn't call NYPD because I didn't fall for his BS.

Without saying this out loud but thinking to myself, hell I can restart my life now instead of in two weeks!

The beautiful highlight of those stressful six months was so gratifying.

As I was exiting the building all of my personal training clients walked out with me.

That's how I got my New York Clientele for the personal training business I immediately started.

Let's all work as hard as we can to not get our panties in a bunch like that man-child.

They aren't worth going to jail for, and you can't fix stupid.

My way of beating this bully was with a smile, intelligence and hard work.

How about you, how do you deal with your stress?... what did you learn and...

What will you add to your tool belt?

____

____

____

____

____

____

____

____

____

#8
Sexy in the City.

Stilettos on the streets of Manhattan.

My feet hurt just thinking about it.

And how about you my friend…how does your feet feel when you remove your shoes?

I hope it's not like this lady.

I had a client who I trained in her apartment in the City that refused to take her six-inch stilettos off until she made her way into her apartment.

I'd seen women wear their sneakers to hoof the streets of the City, then put their heels on when they arrived at work and or home.

No, not this one.

She would literally hobble into her apartment, moaning and groaning and writhing in pain.

She'd remove her shoes and her feet would still be in the same position as if she had her spikes on.

It would take 15 minutes for her to put the heels of her feet on the floor, screaming the entire frickin' time.

I asked her a few times, if she'd considered wearing sneakers to walk the dozen New York City blocks and she was adamant about wearing her heels.

So be it, her workouts were 45 minutes, not an hour, and I stopped asking.

Your feet are to furthest extremity from your heart. Bad circulation from diabetes, obesity, and being sedentary affects our health in so many negative ways.

Do your feet swell, are your calves and feet discolored from blood pooling in your lower extremities?

If so, that's something that should be addressed.

With my health history of diabetes and both of my feet being crushed in motorcycle accidents, I massage my lower legs and my feet daily.

Your feet are your foundation, and you know what happens if your foundation is weak? Your house will crumble.

So, no matter what your footwear choices are—shit-kickers, sneakers, or your sexy stilettos—put healthy feet in them and don't neglect your foundation.

We can't afford to.

How about you, what have you learned and…

What will you add to your tool belt?

#9
Can you kill it?

I'm not talking about a cockroach, a spider or a fly.

But if you pack a firearm, then you should have an answer to this question.

Over the last few years, I've met women at events that carry firearms.

I'm not going to name anyone, but they get no target practice, active shooting drills, or clean their weapons. Ever.

For your safety and the rest of us...I don't want your weapon to just be a piece of jewelry, but something that you can properly use if your life depends on it, and not taken away from you and used to kill you.

After one of my talks, I spoke with a lady that said she couldn't kill one of God's creatures.

Then I asked her, "what if the person is trying to kill one of your children or a family member?" Her response was the same.

Well obviously, you don't have to agree with folks, but

you can respect the fact that they have the right to act or not act, to say their peace and have a different opinion.

On the other hand, I don't go around looking for trouble but if it's either them or me, you might hurt me, cut me, or kill me, but I'm not going down without a fight.

I've said it before and I'll say it again, this world is frickin' nuts and if shit hits the fan, can you kill it?

If not, don't carry it.

Any weapon you carry in a life-or-death situation, if you have to pull it, use it!

As we know, life ain't always sunshine and rainbows, but your life and your family are worth defending if shit goes south.

I will.

How about you, what have you learned and...

What will you add to your tool belt?

____

____

____

____

#10
Use it or lose it.

Stretching

One of the important parts of an exercise regimen that's most neglected or done incorrectly.

I learned that the hard way.

After a few tight muscle mishaps, I stretch daily now, even when I'm traveling and 99% of my travel is by motorcycle.

I stretch in my tent when I'm camping and in my hotel room...and no gym is necessary.

Here's a few stretch tips:

For the best results, stretch when your body is warmed up and hold your stretch at least for 20 to 30 seconds.

You will feel a bit of tightness, but it shouldn't be painful.

If you feel pain, decrease the intensity of your stretch.

Think of your body as a piece of spaghetti...when it's cooked, it's supple and of course uncooked, it'll snap, crackle and pop.

I've been stretching consistently for four decades.

I spend 20 to 30 minutes stretching after my daily workout routines.

On occasion, when I'm really pressed for time, I'll stretch for 15 minutes, and add an additional 15 minutes after a hot shower before bed.

Stretching helps my body recover from just living.

I feel it helps my muscles, ligaments, and tendons elongate which can help lessen the possibility of a severe injury.

The benefit I feel with just a few minutes a day is priceless and you're never too old to start.

Times a passin' anyway, might as well add something into your life that can help you stay healthier longer.

Here's to stretching and to being a sexy senior.

How about you, what have you learned and...

What will you add to your tool belt?

____

____

____

#11
Fountain of youth.

There is so much conflicting information about how much water to drink daily.

Please keep this in mind, no one should know your body better than you.

There are people that drink a gallon or more of water a day.

But that might not work for you.

Have no fear…I'm here to share my little episode of Momma D's red dookie, hydration hack.

It happened back in the early 90's.

I went to a health workshop in Montana where we ate only foods that were grown or raised on their land.

One evening we were served an enormous bowl of shredded beets that looked amazing, so I helped myself to several servings.

And everyone followed suit.

The next morning at breakfast, the ladies were quiet, with a distressed look on their faces.

I broke the ice and asked, "Was your shit red this morning?"

Everyone said, "YES!"

We'd all thought we were shitting blood.

And the reason for this little shitty story is…I found out, if you eat beets, your bowl movement can be red and that's okay but if your urine is red, you are dehydrated.

I eat beets on a regular basis now for the health benefits, but I'll also check my urine to see if I'm hydrated.

Living in the desert, I drink a substantial amount of water daily with added sea salt.

Everyone is different.

As I said earlier, "It's up to you to know your body."

Here are a few hydration hacks for you:

For every cup of coffee, drink a cup of water.

For every glass of wine, or every 4-6 oz. of hard liquor, drink two cups of water.

For every 12 oz. of beer, drink two cups of water.

Now remember, your urine should never be dark, and if you eat beets, your stool will be a bit colorful, but your pee shouldn't be.

Cheers.

How about you, what have you learned and...

What will you add to your tool belt?

#12
Butt print in your couch.

Is there an imprint of your ass in your couch?

My butt was a couch in my mid 20's.

Yes, I had a lot of cushion for the pushin', but my failing health was the real issue.

At such a young age, I already high blood pressure and wore a tight size 16.

I knew if I didn't do something to change my unhealthy lifestyle, I was going to die young like the rest of my family.

The shit I'd done to myself caused a rapid decline in my health and I saw only one way out.

I had to make lifesaving changes in short time.

My first step to start living a healthier lifestyle was to quit the Rock 'n Roll Band I was in.

As the lead singer, drugs and alcohol were always free and I took as much as I wanted to ingest.

Without any knowledge of what to do, I thought running would be a good start.

Well, my enthusiastic health journey began with a blue polyester-jogging suit with white stripes.

Yes, it was the mid-eighties, baby.

I'm grateful there weren't any video cameras rollin', because it was a pitiful sight.

My mind was willing, but my body said, "WTF?!"

But it was time to get it on.

There was no warmup, no anything...I just started running.

Lawd a mercy, I don't know how long I was out, but I do recall my so-called run/jog turned into the ugliest, stumbling, mouth open, about to pass out, sweating bullets, knee buckling, wobble and I didn't even make it around the block.

9-1-1 wasn't called but I was close to needing some serious assistance.

The next morning my feet and ankles had swollen so badly I had to crawl to the bathroom, and I almost pissed my pants.

After that memorable catastrophe, I was a woman on a mission to get healthy.

From where I started to where I am today, is nothing short of a miracle.

It started harsh as hell, but I never stopped.

And what I look like today is a side effect of all the work I've put in seven days a week for years.

Now if there's a butt print in your couch and you're good with that, you do you, but if you're unhappy and unhealthy, just start moving a few minutes a day, a little goes a long way.

Whatever you choose, make it fun and be your best you.

I do.

How about you, what have you learned and…

What will you add to your tool belt?

____

____

____

____

____

____

#13
Surviving stupid people/stupid shit people say.

I know, it's not PC to call anyone stupid, but as you can see, Momma D. ain't PC.

Let's jump right into the deep end.

I'm only going to share one example of stupidity.

You already know, my complete list would be far too long to recite.

This vile encounter happened in 2021, with a dick wad whose mother and father could have been brother and sister.

It was 3:00 a.m., and I hear a loud argument outside my apartment door, the kind that could have easily escalated into punches or gunshots.

I looked through the curtain and saw three people.

One guy was not involved in the hostile aggressive argument, but the other inbred MF was screaming and cussing at a young female.

Needing to get my sleep before rolling out at o-dark-thirty

on a motorcycle road trip, I opened the door gradually, not to startle the already angry asshole.

I asked, "Could you please keep it down? I'd really appreciate it. Thank you."

The butthead that was abusing the young female, turned immediately, made eye contact with me and said, "Get your Nigger ass back inside!"

A horrible gut-wrenching anger jarred my soul, but I was outnumbered and thought it best not to continue the interaction with the moronic, racist, pea-brain.

In short, the shouting did eventually stop, and I lived to ride another day.

Surviving stupid people and the stupid shit they say, in some cases, it's best just to walk away.

Many of us will have encounters with people that should not reproduce, and to the folks that think this racist bullshit doesn't still exist, oh yes it does.

We can't fix stupid, or duct tape folks mouths shut but we can rise above the bullshit and acknowledge it to help us.

Together we can rise and shine on.

I choose to rise.

How about you, how do you deal with stupidity, what have you learned and…

What will you add to your tool belt?

#14
Did you bust one?

I'm talking about self-doubt roadblocks and how the damage can be devastating, if you succumb.

To better cope, growing up, I filled my time with activities to help keep my self-doubt roadblocks somewhat at bay.

I admit, I wasn't self-confident, and I wasn't the best at everything, but I put my best into everything.

The roadblocks in our lives can either break us, block us, or force us to build a foundation of strength that will enable us to either sidestep, leap over, or blast all of them down.

Growing up in the 60's and 70's, in a segregated town, there were many roadblocks, but I vividly remember these speed bump hurdles that I somehow found the courage to faced fearlessly.

When I started in the high school band in the 7th grade, I was the last chair flute player but that wasn't the end I wanted to be on.

I wanted to be 1st chair on the opposite side of the band room and the stage for concerts.

I told the Band Director what I wanted to do, and he said, "You'll have to challenge every chair in front of you."

"Yes sir," I said.

Each chair was a roadblock that had to be moved out of my way and it was on!

There were eight flautists, and my first challenge was for chair number seven.

I practiced extremely hard, and she still beat me, but I wasn't defeated.

After that loss...every week, I challenged for the next chair in front of me.

And you'll be happy to know, my first challenge was my only loss.

By the eighth grade, I was 1st chair and my senior year, I was also the Drum Major of the Band.

I could have easily sat in the eight chairs, waiting for those in front of me to graduate but somewhere deep inside of me I had a burning desire to be better.

Whether our roadblocks are physical and/or psychological, we cannot let anything, or anyone block us from our best life.

It's roadblock blasting time baby!

Let's do this.

How about you, what have you learned and...

What will you add to your tool belt?

#15
700-hundred-pound vibrator.

Warning...if sexual content is offensive to you for religious or other reasons, I strongly suggest you skip #15!

This sexual content includes masturbation...

And for those who choose to indulge, proceed with caution—there's about to be some grown ass shit up in here.

Welcome to the uncomfortable zone.

I'm not going to pigeonhole anyone, but if the hand or vibrator fits, smile baby because we are about to go deep.

But on the other hand, and pardon the pun, there are those folks, perhaps even reading this, that present a so-called squeaky-clean public persona but are freaks behind closed doors.

If that's your thing, cool...it's none of my business.

If you've chosen to read this far, please keep your hypocritical opinions to yourself.

I've come across this many times as a trainer working in

homes. I saw and heard things that would be perfect for today's BS reality shows.

The stories I could tell could be an entirely different book, but the names wouldn't be mentioned to protect me from being sued.

In a few of the Stepford Wives-type neighborhoods, I trained...wife-swapping was prevalent.

Yes, white-collar suburbia—the same people that looked down their noses at folks in a lesser tax bracket and they sure weren't shy about being self-proclaimed elitist snobs.

When I first started going into their homes, I told them, "I'm here to train you not to clean your house."

Being the first black person, ever in their homes, I had to let 'em know.

Now back to #15's title: 700-pound vibrator.

Masturbation...hot damn, I've read that it has health benefits.

Hey, hey, now...as a sexual, single woman, that's good news. Because not now nor in the near future do I need Dick in my life to be satisfied.

But if, or when that time comes, dude, you better carbo-load, hope there's a sale on your little blue pills, be well rested and stretch...because you will know that God is a Black Woman, because all you will be saying is, "Oh God, Oh God!"

You think I'm joking? I'm serious as a boil on your butt.

Now here's a question for you:

For anyone who rides or has ridden a motorcycle...have you ever had an orgasm on your motorcycle while it was rolling?

I have.

Hell, after reading this, there may be some new riders/motorcycle purchases to come.

Once again, pardon the pun.

I'm having a bit fun sharing this real deal shit and I hope you are too.

And if you thought #15 was going to be a how-to training session, think again, because that would an additional charge.

Cash only!

All funnin' aside.

I have more years behind me than I do in front of me, and I'm not going to spend my remaining years worrying or concerning myself about anyone's opinion of me or about how I choose to live my life.

Life is fleeting and there are no do-overs, - so whether you're pitchin' a tent, bush-wackin', polishin' the pencil, or riding a 700-pound vibrator...do you boo, and for the last time, pardon the pun, do it till you're satisfied, I do.

How about you, what have you learned and...

What will you add to your tool belt?

____

____

____

____

____

____

____

____

____

#16
Walk this way.

For me, second to dancing is walking.

I've always been one to take the stairs and not the escalator or moving walkway.

And here's another sucking wind story for you – minus the blue polyester-jogging suit.

I lived in New Jersey; the elevation is 95 feet above sea level and unbeknownst to me the altitude in Albuquerque, New Mexico is a whoppin' 5321!

Hell, I'd hoofed the streets of Manhattan when I had my personal training business.

I'd fight traffic into the City, park my jeep in the 86th street garage on the upper westside...walk up to 96th street, then down to 76th carrying weights in an ammo can.

In between this madness, I'd run in Central Park with a client before returning to my vehicle to drive back to Jersey.

Oh, I thought I was the shit.

Now that I look back, it was more like warm diarrhea.

New York City's elevation is only 33 feet above sea level and day one, when I moved October 2001 - New Mexico, kicked my ass.

My apartment was on the 4th floor...and I had no clue what elevation can do to you.

Of course, after a short minute, I was kind of walking, as I carried things up the stairs instead of putting everything in the elevator.

Bad idea. I thought I was going to pass out.

I was lightheaded, dizzy, finding it very difficult to breath and I was nauseous, at the same time.

It was an extremely challenging, exhausting, WTF day and after about six weeks of living at elevation, I eventually acclimated.

A year later, I spoke with an old lifting partner back in Jersey.

I asked him if he'd like to work out with me when I returned to visit...he immediately said, "Hell no, you live at high altitude, you were bad enough at sea level!"

Here's a 'walk this way' health tip for you to know and another good reason to take the stairs, even just a few.

- Going up the stairs is good for blood pressure and going down is good for blood sugar.

When you're movin' you're winnin'.

I love my dancing, walking and stairs.

How about you, what have you learned and…

What will you add to your tool belt?

#17
Black does crack.

I am not a fan of the saying.

Black does crack, yes in my case, that's an understatement.

I started crackin' in my mid 20's.

Not ever doing anything halfway, I consumed an extreme amount of alcohol, cocaine, partied all night and slept all day.

I also ate like shit, and it showed...heavy stage make-up had its work cut out.

I was knocking on deaths door.

The final straw was when my nose started bleeding on stage, two people I knew died of overdoses, and they consumed less drugs than I did.

I was killing myself, and for what...the Groupies and Klingons that followed you and jumped ship when you're no longer around, then started clinging onto the next band.

No thank you!

I came to realized...that business will kill you if you let it.

And after all of the excess, it is amazing how much damage your body can withstand, and how unbelievably amazing it can repair when you start taking care of it.

Once I cleaned up my life in 1985, I never looked back.

So, it does piss me off when someone tries to be-little all the hard work I've put into myself to be healthy and say black don't crack.

Hey, if you are a person that can eat whatever you want, drink excessively, not exercise and still be poppin', that is awesome, but that's not me.

Hell, I used to crack worse than pork rinds, back in the day.

I partied like a rock star, but now I'm a consistent work-in-progress.

I've staved off a lot of the damage I inflicted on myself, and now I'm shinin' like the Diamond that I am.

How about you, have you partied like a Rock Star?—what have you learned and...

What will you add to your tool belt?

____

____

#18
Your biggest organ.

Your skin.

I'm asked all the time, what do you use on your skin?

Well, here it is...Momma D's Magic.

I use Tahitian noni juice and olive oil on my face daily and I've been using both for years.

First I put a teaspoon of Tahitian noni on a cotton pad and a teaspoon of Extra Virgin Olive oil on my face in the morning and before bed at night.

I also exfoliate my face with olive oil and brown sugar or coffee grounds.

When I'm on the road, a couple of days a week, I use olive oil with one of the little packets of sugar or the coffee grounds in my hotel room.

I continue to tell whoever asks, it's not what you put on your face and body, but what you put in it.

Your daily healthy high-octane food/fuel and proper hydration with water, not soda or sugary drinks is a great start.

Over the years, I've observed a lot of folks doing things in reverse with all the creams and so-called miracle potions.

You can't eat like shit, not exercise, smoke and drink and expect miracles from the creams.

On the flip side, the cosmetic and pharmaceutical companies will love you.

It blew my mind, when I worked in Manhattan…one of the gyms would give Botox injections before the clients worked out.

And shortly after that, just for shits and giggles, I went inside a mall to check out the prices of the anti-aging face-emollients.

Damn, the prices were outrageous!

Lawd a mercy, I'd rather spend that kind of cash on healthy food and gas for my motorcycle.

Just calling it the way I see it.

Here's another Momma D's skin care do's for you…

I also dry skin brush my entire body five minutes daily before my shower which helps to detoxify my skin by increasing blood circulation and promoting lymph flow/drainage.

My triple threat is...olive oil, Tahitian noni juice and dry skin brushing for my biggest organ, my skin.

As you continue reading through the numbers, you'll learn so much more about what I do.

Please remember...If you haven't been consistent with what you've started doing for at least six weeks, don't add something else.

You're creating good habits that takes time and consistency is key.

True health is a marathon not a sprint and it's from the inside - out.

Even if you choose one thing from this Handbook and do it for the rest of your life, you'll be better.

Yes, I know that some of you will of course, pick #15!

How about you, what have you learned and...

What will you add to your tool belt?

____

____

____

____

#19
Ice bath.

More of Momma D's do's...but an ice bath isn't one of them.

Ice baths are beneficial for recovery, but I'll stick to Epsom salt baths and infrared sauna sessions for relaxation and recovery plus the following…

- I massage my lower legs and feet with essential oils… lavender, peppermint, and tea tree mixed with olive oil, daily.

- My sleep is high priority – good quality sleep is the number one way to boost your immune system. – and to help my quality of sleep…there's no screentime an hour before bed. - I sleep in a dark, cool bedroom. - I sleep under a Nikken infrared quilt and on a Nikken mattress with magnets.

- I find it interesting that eating healthy and quality sleep wasn't prescribed for our health to kick Covid's ass.

My friend, if you haven't really put an effort into being healthier, there's a lot more than just Covid out there, and a strong immune system will help to stave off or recover better from frickin' monkey pox, flu, and God knows what else we're going to be faced with.

Whether it's an ice bath or whatever you choose for your recovery to build a strong defense system that willwithstand the onslaught of things attacking our mind, bodies, and spirits.

Getter done.

I do.

How about you, what have you learned and…

What will you add to your tool belt?

___

___

___

___

___

___

___

___

___

#20
Your best piece.

Your brain.

Food for thought…

What we consume doesn't flow from only the neck down, it also goes to our brain.

I have known this for years but after what happened to me, my focus on brain health heightened.

On July 1, 2020, I sustained permanent brain damage after getting blasted by a car while I was riding my motorcycle, MAGIC.

Once again, I was a woman on a mission…my recovery and healing were at the top of the list.

My first and I'd say one of the most important things I did, I eliminated negative people, thoughts and things from my life.

I changed the time of my last meal of the day by consuming my food four hours before bed.

My hydration became more important.

I found out the hard way, one month after I was hit.

When I don't consume enough water, I now get headaches.

Please remember our bodies are a complete unit.

What you eat, drink and think affects your brain too.

Besides the horrible headaches, on several occasions after the accident, the concussion I sustained, and vertigo affected every aspect of my life.

I forgot how to ride my motorcycle.

I don't own a car and haven't since 2014, and my motorcycle is my only form of transportation.

It was unfathomable.

My brain couldn't comprehend how to do what had been second nature to me before the accident. The uncertainty of my ability to ride was like nothing I'd ever felt.

I was scared.

For weeks, I literally had such bad anxiety attacks before I'd kick my leg over my girl, MAGIC.

Each time before we rolled, I'd stand next to her and repeat to myself, "You've ridden hundreds of thousands of miles, you can do this."

Repeatedly, I spoke it out loud and after a few minutes I'd get in the saddle, shaking, but as soon as we started to roll all the doubts, anxiety, and nerves melted away.

Defeating this demon and utilizing all the brain cells it takes to operate a motorcycle is good exercise for the brain.

I take a different way home now, I read more and to be able to write this book for you was amazingly therapeutic and a true blessing.

After fine tuning things a bit, I feel I have improved significantly.

I'm not and may never be like I was before the accident, but you can be guaranteed...every day, I'm going to be my best me I can be!

Our amazing brain...please don't take it for granted.

I don't.

How about you, what have you learned and...

What will you add to your tool belt?

____

____

____

#21
Stuff your Pie-hole.

Are you a happy, sad, social, all of the above, or none of the above…eater?

Do you eat when you're not hungry?

I used to say, "If there's no chocolate in heaven, I'm not going."

And Snicker's bars were my favorite.

I'd like to share an experience with Snicker's I'll never forget and I don't think you will either.

Have you ever gotten drunk, prayed to the porcelain God that you'd never drink again, and did?

Yes, I've done that too, but this time with Snicker's bars and in a hospital delivery room.

Here we go…

Almost time to pop pregnant, I had just slammed an enormous amount of bite sized Snicker's and the contractions started.

I was 18 years. old, living home with my mom, and the nearest hospital was 10 miles away.

We didn't have a car, so a friend had to drive us.

When we arrived, I was immediately rolled into the delivery room, and I threw up Snicker's bars. It was so bad; they were also coming out of my nose.

The doctor was scolding me, saying I shouldn't have eaten.

When I look back on it, I should have faced him and covered him with nuts, caramel and chocolate.

Not only did I blow chow, but I also shit myself...my hair was looking all cute going in and after natural childbirth, I came out looking like Don King.

No, I didn't stop eating Snicker's bars for years, but I have recognized, I am an emotional 'happy' eater.

Happy times have in the past, brought on episodes of devouring chocolate covered almonds. Not just a few either, weighing them on a scale was more like it.

Thank goodness, eating healthier has helped to lessen my ravenous cravings.

These days I don't eat Snicker's bars anymore or chocolate covered almonds but occasionally I will have some bacon.

Like the Snicker's bars, the bacon tastes great going in but the next morning, I can't fart with confidence.

Over time, our taste buds and the body/machine will change but don't ever try to be perfect.

Remember it's a marathon not a sprint.

I hear people say cheat meal, but I call it a treat.

Live an 80/20 life.

If you can eat healthy 80% or more, that's fantastic.

And please don't scrimp on your treat!

Eat it, enjoy it, make it orgasmic and after your eyes have stopped rolling back in your head, continue with your healthy lifestyle.

Remember my friend…the stress you put on yourself for eating an unhealthy food, 'once in a while' is more detrimental to your health than the food you ate.

Enjoy!!!

And for the last time…once in a while' isn't the shit that's going to shorten your quality of life and your years.

I believe.

How about you, what have you learned and…

What will you add to your tool belt?

#22
You packin'?

We carry too much shit when we travel, and I'm a prime example of this when I first started riding cross-country on my motorcycle.

100-pounds would have been a conservative estimate of my gear load.

When I decided to travel on twos, I didn't have anyone to ask or to give me any advice.

But after trial and error and many miles in the saddle, I think I have a clue now but I'm always working to be more efficient.

Whether it's for two or three days, a week, a month or six months…my pack list varies very little.

This may seem like a lot, but each item takes up very little space, the weight is minimal and for my piece of mind, it works for me.

Here is my motorcycle cross-country list:

Three – t-shirts
Two – long sleeve tops for layering

Three – pairs of socks (I wear two pair at a time because of my feet being damaged from motorcycle accidents)
Three – pairs of legging (I wear under my riding pants)
Toiletries
Vitamins
Protein Powder and mixer
Spices
Water
Water filter
Coffee cup
Accident Scene Management First aid kit
Small mirror
Sports tape
Small Nikken Magnets
Small compressor
Small container of dish soap
Plug kit
Tools
Flashlight (One that also has a flasher for emergencies)
Motorcycle Owner's manual
One pair of summer gloves
One pair of leather gloves with long gauntlets
Gerbing's heated gloves (used for 32 degrees or below)
Gerbing's heated jacket liner
Thermals – top and bottom
Zip ties
Duct tape
Toilet paper
Air gauge
Tripod
Laptop
Sunglasses

Rain gear
Extra batteries
Extra key fob
Extra fuses
Small Sewing kit
Tarp
Snacks – almond & walnuts
Bug spray

When I camp, I also pack a one-person tent, small hammer and a sleeping bag that's packs to the size a football. (No mattress pad)

My left saddle bag is for my emergency gear and things I don't need daily.

The right is for the things I need access to like food, water, tripod, gloves etc.

My top case is for my tarp, clothes, toiletries, vitamins and protein powder.

I make sure my saddle bags are equal in weight and the top case is low-profile for better balance and less wind drag.

This list could be for a week or six weeks, the only thing I'd add is more vitamins and protein…and replenish my snacks along the way.

Packing for a plane, I only travel with a carry on and a shoulder purse or helmet bag.

I bring clothes that can be mixed and matched, enabling me to have several looks with less baggage.

I don't watch YouTube videos for how-to or what-to carry and how to pack.

Packing is personal.

I've found what works best for me and you can too.

Most importantly just have fun.

That's what it's all about, right?

Before #22 ends, here's a couple of my clothes-drying tips:

Roll your clothes up in a bath towel to pull out excess moisture. They will hang dry quicker. - Or throw in a dry bath towel with your clothes in the dryer and they will dry faster.

I'm continuing to learn even after all these years and miles.

I love evolving whether I'm soaring in the air or on twos.

How about you, what have you learned and…

What will you add to your tool belt?

____

____

#23
Breaking free from DV.

Domestic Violence.

For years, I was suicidal because of it and no one believed it was happening to me.

To survive, I became numb to the abuse I endured growing up as a child, and in my marriage.

So many of us have and continue to suffer in silence.

And it's not just happening to women, there are men suffering too.

The scars, whether physical or phycological are tremendous weights we carry and some-how, some-way needs to be expelled so we don't pass it on to our children and the world.

Does this sound familiar to you?

Never being right, always being accused of something you didn't do.

You cringe when you hear their footsteps.

Your hand is being held by your spouse like a leash, not with love.

You're isolated and feel lost.

And if this is all you've ever known throughout your life, breaking free sounds impossible, but it is possible.

The lack of self-esteem I carried from my childhood made me a perfect candidate for further abuse as an adult, because abuse was familiar.

It was a blessing in disguise that my ex ran out on me. I was also blessed to have a friend to finally talk to that didn't judge or dismiss my pain, frustration, and hopelessness.

There are no simple answers or quick fixes to break free from domestic violence.

If possible, find someone that you can talk to, and know I am here for you.

Please remember as well, when you're out of the abusive relationship, there's still work to be done.

Learning to love yourself and to begin to fix what's broken inside, whether it's with therapy, counseling or a friend, don't be afraid to ask for help.

My mission is to continue to donate money to domestic violence shelters, and I will continue my own personal healing journey and pass on my love to as many people as possible and make a difference through my experiences.

I believe.

How about you, if this is you, what have you learned and…

What will you add to your tool belt?

___

___

___

___

___

___

___

___

___

#24
Living large on less.

Small space huge life.

When I decided to move the Las Vegas, Nevada, by October 2022, it was the perfect opportunity to get rid of things that were ultimately weighing me down.

Once my decision was made, I gave myself a year to make it happen.

I started immediately selling items and giving things away.

Not all at once, but I vowed to get rid of something every day, something as small as a picture fame but daily something had to go.

Over the months, I was shocked at all the shit I had accumulated in that apartment.

Then bam, 2021 had come to an end and my clean out the place pace had accelerated.

Still not knowing how all of this was going to play out, I kept pushing.

In January 2022, I was chosen as one of the Top 100

Women in Powersports, and the awards luncheon was in Vegas.

It was time to roll to Vegas.

While I was in town, I also celebrated my 64th birthday and I was invited to a private party by a friend of mine, Mario, in Henderson, Nevada.

At the party, I told Karen, our beautiful hostess and Mario's Lady, I wanted to move to Vegas.

Immediately she told me her nephew Carmen is a realtor.

Karen gave him my number and Carmen contacted me within days with an extensive list of properties.

I was already back Albuquerque, and now it was time to ride my motorcycle back in three months.

Upon my return to Las Vegas, Carmen had scheduled viewings for a couple of suites in the Signature at MGM Grand.

Immediately when I walked in, I loved the energy of the place.

I'd already decided suburbia wasn't my thing and this location and atmosphere was Momma D. I wanted to vibe with the city's energy, and as an extra bonus, everything was within walking distance.

Only one suite was available for viewing that day and the view from that penthouse wasn't what I was looking for. It didn't have a balcony and it was out of my price range.

It was time for plan B.

With my heavy travel schedule of speaking engagements and book signings across the country, I needed a place that was furnished as well.

I was not going to take furniture from my apartment in New Mexico or furnish a new place...that wouldn't be feasible.

After my viewing, I rode back home and continued to eliminate items, in between appearances in Woodstock, Illinois, Chicago, Illinois, Kansas City, Missouri, Durango, Colorado and York, Pennsylvania.

Lo and behold, in the middle of all my crazy, cross-country stuff, Carmen sent me an email for another suite that became available at the Signature.

It had a balcony, beautiful view, jacuzzi tub and was furnished, plus the price was right.

We were rollin'...

In May of 2022, we closed on my new home in Vegas baby.

I'd eliminated over 95% of my belongings before the move...with the help of my son Miguel, his truck, a few of my belongs and my motorcycle, I am living large on less.

It is such a freeing feeling to ditch a lot of baggage.

And I love my uncluttered life.

How about you, what have you learned and…

What will you add to your tool belt?

____

____

____

____

____

____

____

____

____

#25
Your success should never stop.

Your legacy.

Sharing your wisdom and experiences with others will last far into the future after you're gone.

This is something I'm very blessed to have done as a coach, mentor, and a Momma.

A few years back, I took a ride into Utah to visit a young man, that I'd trained when he was a fighter at a Mixed Martial Arts gym Albuquerque.

Travis had opened his own gym and wanted me to come and see it.

Travis was not only a professional MMA fighter and high-level wrestler, he'd also been a Utah State Police Motor Patrol Officer.

On the day I arrived, I was greeted with his big ear-to-ear smile and the best hug.

He immediately introduced me to his students as his coach that used to kick his butt.

As the class started, I stood and observed as he was instructing…I noticed something that brought a smile to my face.

He had his class doing some of the same exercises I'd used on him.

Travis saw that I noticed. He smiled and said, "they work."

That was one of the best compliments I could have ever asked for.

I told him that's great, that is respect.

I coached you; you're paying it forward and a part of us will live on forever.

For every young man that I've coached: fighters, Police Officers and soldiers, my job doesn't end when the physical and psychological training is completed.

I've not only trained them for battle but to be good human beings after their missions' end.

Our true success is what we bring to the world, shared with love in a non-selfish way.

Until our last breath, we can continue to pay it forward. We can inspire our youth so that they may pass it on and a part of us will continue to inspire through eternity.

How about you, what have you learned and…

What will you add to your tool belt?

#26
Come and get it.

Our nutrition…health is the goal and weight loss is the side-effect.

And speaking of a huge health life changer, the book *Eat Right 4 your Type* is the absolute best thing I can attribute to my nutrition and health success.

I've read the entire book countless times and found it very informative for achieving optimum health.

Dr. Peter J. D'Adamo and his father before him, with years of research, have in my opinion, nailed it.

This is not a diet!

If you know me, you know I don't believe in frickin' diets.

People diet, stop and gain more weight than they lost.

Within weeks of beginning my, eat right for my blood type journey, my health started to improve.

Matter of fact, I've helped fighters make weight, by having them eat according to their blood type. They never had to starve to make weight and could eat their food/fuel right before stepping on the scale.

Folks seem to think there's only one thing I do to be healthy, but this book will squash that narrow-minded thinking.

And when I was asked for the umpteenth time, "Do you do Paleo?"

"No!" I replied. "I've been eating right for my blood type since the early 90's."

"Does it work?" she asked.

Help me out here...would you bitch-slap her for me, please?

Yes, it frickin' works!

Now it's time to move on to the nitty-gritty, with more of Momma D's daily health habits:

I consume two – three tablespoons of Apple Cider Vinegar in water daily and I add a cup to my bath water, 2 – 3 times a week.

I add a pinch of sea salt to my water to help replenish my electrolytes.

I consume garlic and onions, as much as possible and I

eat as many colors of foods possible—green, yellow, orange, white, purple, red, you get the point.

I love my salmon, sardines in water, eggs, buffalo, beef, elk, venison and my favorite is lamb.

I add walnuts, pecans, Brazil nut and almonds to salads and as snacks.

Another little tip for you: soak your nuts—the almond that is—because your body will be able to digest them better.

It's time to continue your fuel/food adventure...

- As you will see in Momma D's Magic recipes there are no exact measurements.
- Perhaps if I write a healthy recipe book in the future, there will be.
- Please feel free to have fun with them.

Enjoy...

Momma D's Magic Smoothie
(I use the original Nutribullet)

Chocolate Protein powder
Beets
Cocoa powder
Vitamin C powder
Spices – cayenne pepper, ginger root, turmeric and

curry powder
Psyllium husks
Fennel seed
Tahitian noni juice
Olive oil
Black strap molasses
Sliced ginger root
Walnuts
Whole fat Greek yogurt
Broccoli
Cauliflower
Carrots
Kale and or spinach
Frozen pineapple and blueberries
Filtered water

Momma D's Magic lamb and sweet potatoes

One pound of ground lamb (you can use ground beef, venison, elk, buffalo or turkey)

Marinate with mushrooms, chopped onion, carrots, olive oil, the same spices that I use for my smoothie and add garlic powder, black strap molasses and filtered water.

Cover your magic and put it in the refrigerator for two – three days, stirring daily.

Cover and slow cook in a skillet, on the stove-top until the juices have cooked down.

Either boil or bake the sweet potatoes, cut and plate them.

Pour your Momma D's Magic meat mixture over the sweet potatoes and enjoy (all to taste)

Momma D's Magic Oatmeal

1 cup of either old-fashion or quick oat
Cook until done
Pour into a bowl
Add chocolate flavored protein powder
Cocoa powder
Black strap molasses
Olive oil

Stir then sprinkle a few raisins on top.

When I started eating according to my blood type, I didn't do everything all at once but the changes that I made, made a huge difference.

Over time, it's become second nature to me and when I travel, it's a huge help as well.

If I'm in a town and there's no restaurant that has food I can eat, I make a run to the grocery store.

My go to is, a large container of spinach.

I add walnuts, olive oil and spices. I'll eat half for dinner and the other half for breakfast.

So, whatever you chose to help your health, it should be something you'll do for a lifetime not a short time.

How about you, what have you learned and...

What will you add to your tool belt?

#27
Sweet Spot.

Is your home your heaven?

Or, where is your sweet spot?

My home for most of my life wasn't my heaven but being in the saddle of my motorcycle was the only time I felt the closest to heaven.

It's taken 64 years, but I am finally happy wherever I am, at home, or out on my motorcycle

Sadly, there are people who have more money than they know what to do with and still don't have a sweet spot, that little niche of spiritual nourishment.

I've been around them.

Here's an example of, the bank roll's full but the soul is empty and cold.

I had a personal training client, whose husband was a big executive for a pharmaceutical company.

Their house was so big, I got lost going to the bathroom.

I had to speak to them using the intercom to find my way back to their gym.

I was told to take a right at the handball court.

Now it's time for, 'the money didn't make him happy' nasty-freak story.

Mr. VP of big pharma would ask his friends if they would have sex with his wife, while he watched from inside the closet.

None of his friends took him up on it and it made for a very unhappy, hostile, nasty vile freak.

His perversions were downright unnerving.

When I'd arrive at their mansion, to train her, he would eerily be sitting in his big chair holding the newspaper up and wouldn't put it down to say hello.

His wife would have to tell him to say hello to me. He'd say hello with a monotone scratchy voice but never lowered the newspaper. I had a feeling there was a hole in that frickin' newspaper.

I get chills thinking about it.

After speaking with the wife during a few of her training sessions, she admitted she was tolerating the BS and stayed for the money.

But no amount of money was worth me returning to their house another day! I gave her a refund and I was done.

There is nothing wrong with having money.

There is something wrong if you're still not happy.

Peace is my sweet spot and as I write this for you, I'm sitting on my balcony with the beautiful Vegas view... yes, my sweet spot too.

If you have a sweet spot, that warms your heart that's fantastic but if not, ask for it and it'll find you.

I believe.

How about you, what have you learned and...

What will you add to your tool belt?

____

____

____

____

____

____

#28
Downsize to rise.

Keep people in your life that push the button for you to go to the penthouse not the basement.

Unfortunately, it could be family members that are looking to cut the cable on the elevator, so you'll come crashing down.

The cold harsh reality hit when I decided to leave Albuquerque and move to Vegas.

Don't get me wrong, I did make solid lifetime friends there, but there was some frickin' hate coming from people I thought were my friends, and that hurt, bad.

I can't wrap my brain around it, but I had a harsh, heart wrenching reality check that they weren't my real friends anyway.

That's the kind of sting that takes more than a minute to get over. But we must.

On to the rise side - my buddy Sergeant Marc Mier of the New Mexico State Motor Patrol showed some mad respect for me.

The morning of my farewell party at Rust is Gold Coffee,

the coolest chill spot in town, Mier said he'd be there, and come hell or high water, he made it.

Let me back up a bit…the Sarge and his wife live in Santa Fe, New Mexico.

And before heading to Albuquerque, his dog got sick, threw up on their carpet, he went and rented a rug cleaner then cleaned to rug.

After finishing up and rolling south on I-25, I don't want to guess what his speed was, but his wife kept saying to him, you need to slow down or you're going to kill us.

He said, "We can't be late!"

Now mind you, there were people that didn't show up that lived in town because it was raining just a little bit.

The actions of people, show you, their truth.

When I say I've made some lifelong friends there… the Sarge is as good as it gets.

People will downsize themselves for you and who remains will continue to have your six, all the way to the penthouse.

No time for scrubs.

How about you, what have you learned and…

What will you add to you tool belt?

#29
Momma D's MAGIC.

My ride or die. My BFF. My girl, MAGIC.

When you almost bite it together, you're forever bonded.

This is a kind of bond we can have with a person, people or vehicle, and in this case it's my motorcycle.

I purchased MAGIC as a birthday present for myself in January 2020.

She's a Black, 2019 BMW R1250 GSA.

Earlier, I've mentioned July 1, 2020, and I am happy I'm here to share with you, the day I'll celebrate, like a new Re-birthday.

Still just getting to know each other over the last few months, our new beginning was almost our end.

On July 1, 2020, I had mailed a copy my first book 50 States of Consciousness at the post office in Tijeras, New Mexico, a few miles east of Albuquerque.

I decided to take a ride up to Madrid, New Mexico, a cool little mining town for a cup of coffee.

I'd ridden 14 North more times than I dare to count but, on this day, it was life-altering.

As I rolled north in the left lane, in the blink of an eye, I saw a car coming out from a side street.

She was already in the right lane, and crossing into my lane turning south traveling at around 50 mph.

The exact moment I saw her I swerved into the turn lane to avoid a direct hit.

My initial speed was 40 mph but after accelerating at the point of impact, her and I were going approximately the same speed.

It was a 100-mph impact.

With less than a second to react, her car blasted MAGIC so hard, it pushed the engine guard into the motor, busted her right saddle bag off, and clipped her rear tire.

I was able to keep us upright and we didn't go down.

No, I didn't go down, but my legs did fly up in the air, and not in a good way.

After the tremendous impact, I got the bike under control…I reached down and that's when I discovered MAGIC's saddlebag was gone.

I pulled my girl off the road and onto the shoulder.

There was a couple that were in a car behind us and witnessed the hit. They could not believe that I was able to keep the bike upright.

The woman that blasted us came back and said, "I'm the one who hit you."

She was shaking and I hugged her and said, "Everything is going to be alright baby."

I'm consoling her and she almost killed me.

But that's me.

The folks that were behind us, called 9-1-1.

Since they heard a motorcycle and car, the Calvary was sent.

A couple of Police Units, ambulance, and fire truck rolled up.

After seeing the damage on MAGIC and the damage to her car...the bumper had a basketball sized dent in the fender. The fender had dislodged from the car, the headlight was busted, and the grill was damaged.

They were not expecting my response.

The paramedic asked me if I went down. I said, "No, if I had you'd be scraping me off the pavement."

Immediately all the first responders started high fiving me, saying that was some badass riding.

But before the accolades started, one of the Officers said, "Most people would have hit their brakes."

I told him, braking wasn't ever my option.

There wasn't any time to think, just react.

After everyone had left, I rode MAGIC to the BMW Dealership in Albuquerque and told the guys I'd just been hit by a car.

"What?" They said, then asked if I was alright and immediately walked outside to inspect the damage.

"Damn, did you go down?" They asked.

I said, "Nope!"

"Your experience saved you." they responded.

The salesmen asked if I wanted to take a loaner bike.

I told them, no thanks.

I just want to get home.

It was the countdown for the 4th of July weekend, and I didn't want to be on the road.

When I returned to my apartment, I sat down...and it hit me.

God is not ready for me yet.

And I'm not wasting another moment...MAGIC and I have a lot more to do together.

Not only was I still alive, but if I'd hesitated, hit my brakes, or had been riding a V-twin motorcycle, instead of that big boxer motor on MAGIC...my right leg would been severed, I would have gone down or much worse.

When I rode MAGIC back to the dealership the following week, I told them, if my girl isn't totaled, repair her.

And as you see, she's gracing the cover of this book, looking wonderful, sexy and badass.

We can't control what others do, but we can do our part to take a bad situation and make them better.

We can help others with your experiences and be a blessing to everyone who crosses our path.

If we all would do this wouldn't the world be such a better place?

YES!

How about you, what have you learned and...

What will you add to your tool belt?

#30
Curtain call.

Before that time comes, let's do as many encores as possible.

My friend, do you have a bucket list?

Or I'd prefer to call it, just do it list.

As we become adults, adulting happens and what remains is a bucket list to do before you die.

Some folks say, "I'll do it when I retire."

Well, if you're not taking care of yourself now, you might not be able to do anything but sit around, woulda, coulda, shoulda-ing until your big dirt nap.

First of all, I'm not retiring until I stop breathing and the thought of rocking in a rocking chair, in the middle of frickin' nowhere, which is what my ex had planned for us, is asinine.

This maybe what some folks want to do but not me baby!

The clock is ticking…

So, before your last curtain call…and please don't wait until you have one foot in the grave and the other on a banana peel.

Your 'just do it' list doesn't have to be long.

Pick something…live it—breath it and just frickin' do it.

I have.

How about you, what have you learned and…

What will you add to your tool belt?

____

____

____

____

____

____

____

____

____

#31
Keep Shinin' Baby.

Not just a phrase but a way of life.

Here's a few enlightening words I heard someone say, "When we are starting to walk, each time we fall, everyone's cheering us on, saying get up, you're doing great.

We get up because everyone is cheering us on but why is it, when we become adults, the opposite happens.

We start a new business or strike out on our own to do something unique, instead of everyone cheering us on, they say, you can't do that."

Yes, the cheers are great, but that shouldn't be why you do what you do.

This is one of the reasons some athletes play past the time their bodies are no longer able to perform at the elite level.

When the cheering stops, some are lost because the cheers are like a drug. They don't think they can shine without it.

This is another reason for us to appreciate what we had, what we have and what we still have to give.

You might not be that Superstar on the field, the court, the stage or in the ring, but it's about being the Superstar in your life.

There is a Superstar in all of us.

We might not get paid the millions, but what we can contribute to the people around us, is priceless.

We shouldn't think less of ourselves because of a dollar amount.

We can...put a smile on someone's face, warm their hearts, love unconditionally, and let our Superstar keep shinin' baby.

I believe.

How about you, what have you learned and...

What will you add to your tool belt?

____

____

____

____

#32
Can you hold it?

Your balance in life.

I'm always being warned about the dangers of riding a Motorcycle, but hell, I'm more concerned about losing my balance, falling and busting my ass in the bathtub.

Callin' 9-1-1 in the tub naked is not good.

In this case, I'm referring to how important balance is as we age.

I incorporate balance training in my life daily and it's

never too late.

I have worked with 90-year-old Seniors in nursing homes, when I was an Exercise Physiologist for Exxon Corporation International in Florham Park, New Jersey.

I worked with them just a few minutes a day and it was great to see their confidence build.

So, we don't have any excuse not to be working a few minutes a day on our balance.

If I'm blessed to be here at 90, I want to be a healthy and strong at 90.

Now I'd like to share 'my 90+ goal routine, that also includes working on my balance:

- I stretch in bed, and I pray.
- I consume a 16 oz. cup of warm water with apple cider vinegar, Vitamin D3 drops and my spices. (Also see #26)
- Immediately after my apple cider vinegar mix, I drink a 16 oz. cup of coffee with olive oil and cocoa powder
- For additional hydration and nutrition, I consume another 16 oz. cup of water with more apple cider vinegar and spices.
- Now it's time to amp up my bodies circulatory system by using my foot massager for 15-minutes.
- Next, I do a vertical leg raise pose or forearm inversion for five minutes…(Also see #5)
- After massage and inversion, I do standing balance work for two - three minutes.
- It's time now for my daily Diamond poses that I've done at home and on the road, since the early 90's…*The Five Tibetan Rites*, or the "Fountain of Youth." They are a series of five yoga poses that are a traditional practice that's been done for more than

2500 years. People perform these *Rites* with the intention of restoring youth and increasing vitality.

- After the completion of the *Rites*, I stretch.

- I continue with my stairs warmup by walking backwards on the treadmill in the gym for 15 minutes ...and proceed to walk/sprint 38 + floors of stairs, in my building - Monday, Wednesday, Friday and Saturday.

- On Tuesday, Thursday and Sunday. I do wall-sits, isometric hamstring curls and planks, five minutes each and 25 tibialis anterior raises.

- I stretch again, before lying on the floor, to help bring my heartrate back down, by stretching my quadriceps while standing which is also for my balance.

- My smoothie or my oatmeal mix are consumed before the stairs.

- After each stairs training sessions, I spend an hour in my infrared sauna.

- Over the course of the day, I ingest the proper amount of water with added salt and consume my food/fuel.

For years I weight trained but as I've gotten older, I've eliminated the weights, implemented the *Rites* and added additional recovery.

In addition to my daily regimen, Chiropractic adjustments and acupuncture treatments have been a staple in health journey for years as well.

As you age, don't hesitate to adjust, what or how you exercise, just don't stop.

Good health is a balance.

So, we should work on having a balanced, enjoyable life, for as long as possible, as strong as possible, with NO dimmer switch.

YES!

How about you, what have you learned and…

What will you add to your tool belt?

____

____

____

____

____

____

____

#33
Momma D. Diamond.

When I hear my name, I still get chills.

After July 1, 2020, I wanted a new beginning.

I didn't want to keep the name I was given at birth because I felt it was my slave name, and I definitely didn't want to keep my ex's last name.

The professional fighters I've trained respectfully call me Momma D., and I felt Diamond was a perfect last name because of the pressure it takes to create one.

After my name change paperwork was completed, the court hearing was set for March 1, 2022, at 9:30 a.m. MST.

It was to be done by phone. Not a Zoom call, but it was official, nevertheless.

It was a judge, court stenographer, my witness and me.

I didn't care that it wasn't a Zoom call.

I sat at my dining room table dressed as if I was in court.

It was that important to me.

The Judge said, "I know this sounds ridicules but please raise your right hand." And I was sworn in.

I was not only dressed for court, but I raised my right hand as if I was as well.

He proceeded with a few more questions and wrapped everything up by saying, "Congratulations, Momma D. Diamond, thank you and have a nice day."

I sat there for a moment and bawled like a baby then I danced, laughed and screamed, "I AM MOMMA D. DIAMOND!"

And if this wasn't enormous enough, two years to the date of my accident July 1, 2020, at 64 years old, I became a first-time homeowner and moved into my new spot in Las Vegas., July 1, 2022!

Now it's time for the Diamond to shine bright in Vegas baby.

My purpose for sharing Momma D's 33 with you is to have a positive dialog with you, help you, bless you, and hopefully enhance your life for many years to come.

You can do whatever you set your mind to.

Put in the work, with passion on purpose baby.

I believe.

How about you, what have you learned and...

What will you add to your tool belt?

There you have it.

Your Momma D's real-life tactics to help you in whatever you do, on and off twos.

It's never too late to create a good habit, starting with being truly happy and at peace.

We don't do coulda, woulda, shoulda's up in here.

Today is the beginning for you to be better than you were yesterday.

Together, let's do this!

And while you're gettin' it done, always, keep shinin' baby.

Huge hugs coming your way when I see you out there somewhere!

Love ya...*Momma D. Diamond*

CPSIA information can be obtained
at www.ICGtesting.com
Printed in the USA
JSHW040509200323
39030JS00010B/1